the happy couple
gratitude journal

The Happy Couple Gratitude Journal
by Gratitude Daily
Published by Creative Ideas Publishing

© 2021 Gratitude Daily

For permissions contact:
permissions@creativeideaspublishing.com

ISBN: 978-1-952016-41-7

"A good marriage isn't something you find; It's something you make."

–Gary Thomas
Author of
The 5 Love Languages

QUICK NOTE FROM THE AUTHOR:

I'm so excited for the benefits you are about to experience from practicing gratitude as a couple!

This journal includes 4 prompts to fill out each day. The prompt "How He" provides space for the wife to share something that she is grateful for that her husband *did* or simply *was* that day. The prompt "How She" provides the same opportunity for the husband to show appreciation towards his wife.

"Her Day" provides space for the wife to jot down something she was most grateful for that day. "His Day" provides the same opportunity for the husband.

XO,
Jori Outlaw

EXAMPLE:

HOW HE	grilled for dinner
HOW SHE	ordered our son's birthday gift
HER DAY	listened to a good podcast
HIS DAY	went for a run in nice weather

TODAY, I'M THANKFUL FOR...

DATE:

HOW HE

HOW SHE

HER DAY

HIS DAY

DATE:

HOW HE

HOW SHE

HER DAY

HIS DAY

DATE:

HOW HE

HOW SHE

HER DAY

HIS DAY

DATE:

HOW HE _____

HOW SHE _____

HER DAY _____

HIS DAY _____

DATE:

HOW HE _____

HOW SHE _____

HER DAY _____

HIS DAY _____

DATE:

HOW HE _____

HOW SHE _____

HER DAY _____

HIS DAY _____

"A successful marriage isn't the union of two perfect people. It's that of two imperfect people who have learned the value of forgiveness and grace." -Darlene Schacht

TODAY, I'M THANKFUL FOR...

DATE:

HOW HE

HOW SHE

HER DAY

HIS DAY

DATE:

HOW HE

HOW SHE

HER DAY

HIS DAY

DATE:

HOW HE

HOW SHE

HER DAY

HIS DAY

DATE:

HOW HE _____

HOW SHE _____

HER DAY _____

HIS DAY _____

DATE:

HOW HE _____

HOW SHE _____

HER DAY _____

HIS DAY _____

DATE:

HOW HE _____

HOW SHE _____

HER DAY _____

HIS DAY _____

"When there is love in a marriage, there is harmony in the home; when there is harmony in the home, there is contentment in the community; when there is contentment in the community, there is prosperity in the nation; when there is prosperity in the nation, there is peace in the world." -Chinese Proverb

TODAY, I'M THANKFUL FOR...

DATE:

HOW HE

HOW SHE

HER DAY

HIS DAY

DATE:

HOW HE

HOW SHE

HER DAY

HIS DAY

DATE:

HOW HE

HOW SHE

HER DAY

HIS DAY

DATE:

HOW HE _____

HOW SHE _____

HER DAY _____

HIS DAY _____

DATE:

HOW HE _____

HOW SHE _____

HER DAY _____

HIS DAY _____

DATE:

HOW HE _____

HOW SHE _____

HER DAY _____

HIS DAY _____

"Always strive to give your spouse the very best of yourself; not what's leftover after you have given your best to everyone else." -Dave Willis

TODAY, I'M THANKFUL FOR...

DATE:

HOW HE

HOW SHE

HER DAY

HIS DAY

DATE:

HOW HE

HOW SHE

HER DAY

HIS DAY

DATE:

HOW HE

HOW SHE

HER DAY

HIS DAY

DATE:

HOW HE _____

HOW SHE _____

HER DAY _____

HIS DAY _____

DATE:

HOW HE _____

HOW SHE _____

HER DAY _____

HIS DAY _____

DATE:

HOW HE _____

HOW SHE _____

HER DAY _____

HIS DAY _____

"It is not a lack of love, but a lack of friendship that makes unhappy marriages." -Fredrich Nietzche

TODAY, I'M THANKFUL FOR...

DATE:

HOW HE _____

HOW SHE _____

HER DAY _____

HIS DAY _____

DATE:

HOW HE _____

HOW SHE _____

HER DAY _____

HIS DAY _____

DATE:

HOW HE _____

HOW SHE _____

HER DAY _____

HIS DAY _____

DATE:

HOW HE _____

HOW SHE _____

HER DAY _____

HIS DAY _____

DATE:

HOW HE _____

HOW SHE _____

HER DAY _____

HIS DAY _____

DATE:

HOW HE _____

HOW SHE _____

HER DAY _____

HIS DAY _____

"Being in a long marriage is a little bit like that nice cup of coffee every morning – I might have it every day, but I still enjoy it." -Stephen Gaines

TODAY, I'M THANKFUL FOR...

DATE:

HOW HE

HOW SHE

HER DAY

HIS DAY

DATE:

HOW HE

HOW SHE

HER DAY

HIS DAY

DATE:

HOW HE

HOW SHE

HER DAY

HIS DAY

DATE:

HOW HE _____

HOW SHE _____

HER DAY _____

HIS DAY _____

DATE:

HOW HE _____

HOW SHE _____

HER DAY _____

HIS DAY _____

DATE:

HOW HE _____

HOW SHE _____

HER DAY _____

HIS DAY _____

"So it's not gonna be easy. It's going to be really hard; we're gonna have to work at this everyday, but I want to do that because I want you. I want all of you, forever, everyday. You and me... everyday." -Nicholas Sparks

TODAY, I'M THANKFUL FOR...

DATE:

HOW HE _____

HOW SHE _____

HER DAY _____

HIS DAY _____

DATE:

HOW HE _____

HOW SHE _____

HER DAY _____

HIS DAY _____

DATE:

HOW HE _____

HOW SHE _____

HER DAY _____

HIS DAY _____

DATE:

HOW HE _____

HOW SHE _____

HER DAY _____

HIS DAY _____

DATE:

HOW HE _____

HOW SHE _____

HER DAY _____

HIS DAY _____

DATE:

HOW HE _____

HOW SHE _____

HER DAY _____

HIS DAY _____

"To be fully seen by somebody, then, and be loved anyhow–this is a human offering that can border on miraculous." -Elizabeth Gilbert

TODAY, I'M THANKFUL FOR...

DATE:

HOW HE

HOW SHE

HER DAY

HIS DAY

DATE:

HOW HE

HOW SHE

HER DAY

HIS DAY

DATE:

HOW HE

HOW SHE

HER DAY

HIS DAY

DATE:

HOW HE _____

HOW SHE _____

HER DAY _____

HIS DAY _____

DATE:

HOW HE _____

HOW SHE _____

HER DAY _____

HIS DAY _____

DATE:

HOW HE _____

HOW SHE _____

HER DAY _____

HIS DAY _____

"Let the wife make the husband glad to come home, and let him make her sorry to see him leave." -Martin Luther

TODAY, I'M THANKFUL FOR...

DATE:

HOW HE

HOW SHE

HER DAY

HIS DAY

DATE:

HOW HE

HOW SHE

HER DAY

HIS DAY

DATE:

HOW HE

HOW SHE

HER DAY

HIS DAY

DATE:

HOW HE _____

HOW SHE _____

HER DAY _____

HIS DAY _____

DATE:

HOW HE _____

HOW SHE _____

HER DAY _____

HIS DAY _____

DATE:

HOW HE _____

HOW SHE _____

HER DAY _____

HIS DAY _____

"Who, being loved, is poor?" -Oscar Wilde

TODAY, I'M THANKFUL FOR...

DATE:

HOW HE

HOW SHE

HER DAY

HIS DAY

DATE:

HOW HE

HOW SHE

HER DAY

HIS DAY

DATE:

HOW HE

HOW SHE

HER DAY

HIS DAY

DATE:

HOW HE _____

HOW SHE _____

HER DAY _____

HIS DAY _____

DATE:

HOW HE _____

HOW SHE _____

HER DAY _____

HIS DAY _____

DATE:

HOW HE _____

HOW SHE _____

HER DAY _____

HIS DAY _____

"What greater thing is there for two human souls, than to feel that they are joined for life–to strength each other in all labor, to rest on each other in all sorrow, to minister to each. other in silent unspeakable memories at the moment of the last parting?" -George Eliot

TODAY, I'M THANKFUL FOR...

DATE:

HOW HE

HOW SHE

HER DAY

HIS DAY

DATE:

HOW HE

HOW SHE

HER DAY

HIS DAY

DATE:

HOW HE

HOW SHE

HER DAY

HIS DAY

DATE:

HOW HE _____

HOW SHE _____

HER DAY _____

HIS DAY _____

DATE:

HOW HE _____

HOW SHE _____

HER DAY _____

HIS DAY _____

DATE:

HOW HE _____

HOW SHE _____

HER DAY _____

HIS DAY _____

"The first to apologize is the bravest. The first to forgive is the strongest. The first to forget is the happiest." -Unknown

TODAY, I'M THANKFUL FOR...

DATE:

HOW HE

HOW SHE

HER DAY

HIS DAY

DATE:

HOW HE

HOW SHE

HER DAY

HIS DAY

DATE:

HOW HE

HOW SHE

HER DAY

HIS DAY

DATE:

HOW HE _____

HOW SHE _____

HER DAY _____

HIS DAY _____

DATE:

HOW HE _____

HOW SHE _____

HER DAY _____

HIS DAY _____

DATE:

HOW HE _____

HOW SHE _____

HER DAY _____

HIS DAY _____

"Love recognizes no barriers. It jumps hurdles,
leaps fences, penetrates walls to arrive at its
destination full of hope." -Maya Angelou

TODAY, I'M THANKFUL FOR...

DATE:

HOW HE

HOW SHE

HER DAY

HIS DAY

DATE:

HOW HE

HOW SHE

HER DAY

HIS DAY

DATE:

HOW HE

HOW SHE

HER DAY

HIS DAY

DATE:

HOW HE _____

HOW SHE _____

HER DAY _____

HIS DAY _____

DATE:

HOW HE _____

HOW SHE _____

HER DAY _____

HIS DAY _____

DATE:

HOW HE _____

HOW SHE _____

HER DAY _____

HIS DAY _____

"When you love someone, you love them as the person they are, and not as you'd like them to be." -Leo Tolstoy

TODAY, I'M THANKFUL FOR...

DATE:

HOW HE _____

HOW SHE _____

HER DAY _____

HIS DAY _____

DATE:

HOW HE _____

HOW SHE _____

HER DAY _____

HIS DAY _____

DATE:

HOW HE _____

HOW SHE _____

HER DAY _____

HIS DAY _____

DATE:

HOW HE _____

HOW SHE _____

HER DAY _____

HIS DAY _____

DATE:

HOW HE _____

HOW SHE _____

HER DAY _____

HIS DAY _____

DATE:

HOW HE _____

HOW SHE _____

HER DAY _____

HIS DAY _____

My husband is my best friend, my greatest support, my biggest comfort, my strongest motivation, my truest smile, my deepest love, my favorite, my forever. He has me. Entirely." -Unknown

TODAY, I'M THANKFUL FOR...

DATE:

HOW HE

HOW SHE

HER DAY

HIS DAY

DATE:

HOW HE

HOW SHE

HER DAY

HIS DAY

DATE:

HOW HE

HOW SHE

HER DAY

HIS DAY

DATE:

HOW HE _____

HOW SHE _____

HER DAY _____

HIS DAY _____

DATE:

HOW HE _____

HOW SHE _____

HER DAY _____

HIS DAY _____

DATE:

HOW HE _____

HOW SHE _____

HER DAY _____

HIS DAY _____

"The goal in marriage is not to think alike, but to think together." -Robert C. Dodds

TODAY, I'M THANKFUL FOR...

DATE:

HOW HE
_____

HOW SHE
_____

HER DAY
_____

HIS DAY
_____

DATE:

HOW HE
_____

HOW SHE
_____

HER DAY
_____

HIS DAY
_____

DATE:

HOW HE
_____

HOW SHE
_____

HER DAY
_____

HIS DAY
_____

DATE:

HOW HE _____

HOW SHE _____

HER DAY _____

HIS DAY _____

DATE:

HOW HE _____

HOW SHE _____

HER DAY _____

HIS DAY _____

DATE:

HOW HE _____

HOW SHE _____

HER DAY _____

HIS DAY _____

"Coming together is a beginning; keeping together is progress; working together is success." -Henry Ford

TODAY, I'M THANKFUL FOR...

DATE:

HOW HE _____

HOW SHE _____

HER DAY _____

HIS DAY _____

DATE:

HOW HE _____

HOW SHE _____

HER DAY _____

HIS DAY _____

DATE:

HOW HE _____

HOW SHE _____

HER DAY _____

HIS DAY _____

DATE:

HOW HE _____

HOW SHE _____

HER DAY _____

HIS DAY _____

DATE:

HOW HE _____

HOW SHE _____

HER DAY _____

HIS DAY _____

DATE:

HOW HE _____

HOW SHE _____

HER DAY _____

HIS DAY _____

"Marriage is a huge investment: of time, of energy
and of emotion. Protect and keep contributing
to your investment." -Karen Gordon

TODAY, I'M THANKFUL FOR...

DATE:

HOW HE

HOW SHE

HER DAY

HIS DAY

DATE:

HOW HE

HOW SHE

HER DAY

HIS DAY

DATE:

HOW HE

HOW SHE

HER DAY

HIS DAY

DATE:

HOW HE

HOW SHE

HER DAY

HIS DAY

DATE:

HOW HE

HOW SHE

HER DAY

HIS DAY

DATE:

HOW HE

HOW SHE

HER DAY

HIS DAY

"Until you learn how to fight together, you will
fight against each other." -Anonymous

TODAY, I'M THANKFUL FOR...

DATE:

HOW HE

HOW SHE

HER DAY

HIS DAY

DATE:

HOW HE

HOW SHE

HER DAY

HIS DAY

DATE:

HOW HE

HOW SHE

HER DAY

HIS DAY

DATE:

HOW HE _____

HOW SHE _____

HER DAY _____

HIS DAY _____

DATE:

HOW HE _____

HOW SHE _____

HER DAY _____

HIS DAY _____

DATE:

HOW HE _____

HOW SHE _____

HER DAY _____

HIS DAY _____

"No relationship is all sunshine, but two people can share an umbrella and survive a storm together." -Anonymous

TODAY, I'M THANKFUL FOR...

DATE:

HOW HE

HOW SHE

HER DAY

HIS DAY

DATE:

HOW HE

HOW SHE

HER DAY

HIS DAY

DATE:

HOW HE

HOW SHE

HER DAY

HIS DAY

DATE:

HOW HE _____

HOW SHE _____

HER DAY _____

HIS DAY _____

DATE:

HOW HE _____

HOW SHE _____

HER DAY _____

HIS DAY _____

DATE:

HOW HE _____

HOW SHE _____

HER DAY _____

HIS DAY _____

"Your marriage vows are most important in those moments when they are most difficult to keep." -Dave Willis

TODAY, I'M THANKFUL FOR...

DATE:

HOW HE

HOW SHE

HER DAY

HIS DAY

DATE:

HOW HE

HOW SHE

HER DAY

HIS DAY

DATE:

HOW HE

HOW SHE

HER DAY

HIS DAY

DATE:

HOW HE _____

HOW SHE _____

HER DAY _____

HIS DAY _____

DATE:

HOW HE _____

HOW SHE _____

HER DAY _____

HIS DAY _____

DATE:

HOW HE _____

HOW SHE _____

HER DAY _____

HIS DAY _____

"There is no more lovely, friendly, and charming
relationship, communion or company than
a good marriage." -Martin Luther

TODAY, I'M THANKFUL FOR...

DATE:

HOW HE _____

HOW SHE _____

HER DAY _____

HIS DAY _____

DATE:

HOW HE _____

HOW SHE _____

HER DAY _____

HIS DAY _____

DATE:

HOW HE _____

HOW SHE _____

HER DAY _____

HIS DAY _____

DATE:

HOW HE _____

HOW SHE _____

HER DAY _____

HIS DAY _____

DATE:

HOW HE _____

HOW SHE _____

HER DAY _____

HIS DAY _____

DATE:

HOW HE _____

HOW SHE _____

HER DAY _____

HIS DAY _____

"Love does not consist of gazing at each other,
but in looking outward together in the same
direction." -Antoine de Saint-Exupery

TODAY, I'M THANKFUL FOR...

DATE:

HOW HE

HOW SHE

HER DAY

HIS DAY

DATE:

HOW HE

HOW SHE

HER DAY

HIS DAY

DATE:

HOW HE

HOW SHE

HER DAY

HIS DAY

DATE:

HOW HE

HOW SHE

HER DAY

HIS DAY

DATE:

HOW HE

HOW SHE

HER DAY

HIS DAY

DATE:

HOW HE

HOW SHE

HER DAY

HIS DAY

"The highest happiness on earth is marriage." -William Lyon Phelps

TODAY, I'M THANKFUL FOR...

DATE:

HOW HE

HOW SHE

HER DAY

HIS DAY

DATE:

HOW HE

HOW SHE

HER DAY

HIS DAY

DATE:

HOW HE

HOW SHE

HER DAY

HIS DAY

DATE:

HOW HE

HOW SHE

HER DAY

HIS DAY

DATE:

HOW HE

HOW SHE

HER DAY

HIS DAY

DATE:

HOW HE

HOW SHE

HER DAY

HIS DAY

"The great marriages are partnerships. It can't be a great marriage without being a partnership." -Helen Mirren

TODAY, I'M THANKFUL FOR...

DATE:

HOW HE

HOW SHE

HER DAY

HIS DAY

DATE:

HOW HE

HOW SHE

HER DAY

HIS DAY

DATE:

HOW HE

HOW SHE

HER DAY

HIS DAY

DATE:

HOW HE _____

HOW SHE _____

HER DAY _____

HIS DAY _____

DATE:

HOW HE _____

HOW SHE _____

HER DAY _____

HIS DAY _____

DATE:

HOW HE _____

HOW SHE _____

HER DAY _____

HIS DAY _____

"A husband and wife may disagree on many things but they must absolutely agree on this: to never, ever give up." -Unknown

TODAY, I'M THANKFUL FOR...

DATE:

HOW HE

HOW SHE

HER DAY

HIS DAY

DATE:

HOW HE

HOW SHE

HER DAY

HIS DAY

DATE:

HOW HE

HOW SHE

HER DAY

HIS DAY

DATE:

HOW HE _____

HOW SHE _____

HER DAY _____

HIS DAY _____

DATE:

HOW HE _____

HOW SHE _____

HER DAY _____

HIS DAY _____

DATE:

HOW HE _____

HOW SHE _____

HER DAY _____

HIS DAY _____

"A successful marriage requires falling in love many times, always with the same person." -Mignon McLaughlin

TODAY, I'M THANKFUL FOR...

DATE:

HOW HE

HOW SHE

HER DAY

HIS DAY

DATE:

HOW HE

HOW SHE

HER DAY

HIS DAY

DATE:

HOW HE

HOW SHE

HER DAY

HIS DAY

DATE:

HOW HE _____

HOW SHE _____

HER DAY _____

HIS DAY _____

DATE:

HOW HE _____

HOW SHE _____

HER DAY _____

HIS DAY _____

DATE:

HOW HE _____

HOW SHE _____

HER DAY _____

HIS DAY _____

"A good marriage is one which allows for change
and growth in the individuals and in the way
they express their love." -Pearl S. Buck

TODAY, I'M THANKFUL FOR...

DATE:

HOW HE

HOW SHE

HER DAY

HIS DAY

DATE:

HOW HE

HOW SHE

HER DAY

HIS DAY

DATE:

HOW HE

HOW SHE

HER DAY

HIS DAY

DATE:

HOW HE _____

HOW SHE _____

HER DAY _____

HIS DAY _____

DATE:

HOW HE _____

HOW SHE _____

HER DAY _____

HIS DAY _____

DATE:

HOW HE _____

HOW SHE _____

HER DAY _____

HIS DAY _____

"True love stands by each other's side on good days
and stands closer on bad days." -Unknown

TODAY, I'M THANKFUL FOR...

DATE:

HOW HE

HOW SHE

HER DAY

HIS DAY

DATE:

HOW HE

HOW SHE

HER DAY

HIS DAY

DATE:

HOW HE

HOW SHE

HER DAY

HIS DAY

DATE:

HOW HE _____

HOW SHE _____

HER DAY _____

HIS DAY _____

DATE:

HOW HE _____

HOW SHE _____

HER DAY _____

HIS DAY _____

DATE:

HOW HE _____

HOW SHE _____

HER DAY _____

HIS DAY _____

"Marriage is not a noun; it's a verb. It isn't something you get. It's something you do. It's the way you love your partner every day." -Barbara De Angelis

TODAY, I'M THANKFUL FOR...

DATE:

HOW HE _____

HOW SHE _____

HER DAY _____

HIS DAY _____

DATE:

HOW HE _____

HOW SHE _____

HER DAY _____

HIS DAY _____

DATE:

HOW HE _____

HOW SHE _____

HER DAY _____

HIS DAY _____

DATE:

HOW HE _____

HOW SHE _____

HER DAY _____

HIS DAY _____

DATE:

HOW HE _____

HOW SHE _____

HER DAY _____

HIS DAY _____

DATE:

HOW HE _____

HOW SHE _____

HER DAY _____

HIS DAY _____

"Marriage stands the test of times when both you and
your spouse work towards making things better. And
we are tested the most when we face adversities. If
you can sail through the adversities as one, as a team,
then you have won half the battle." -Unknown

TODAY, I'M THANKFUL FOR...

DATE:

HOW HE

HOW SHE

HER DAY

HIS DAY

DATE:

HOW HE

HOW SHE

HER DAY

HIS DAY

DATE:

HOW HE

HOW SHE

HER DAY

HIS DAY

DATE:

HOW HE _____

HOW SHE _____

HER DAY _____

HIS DAY _____

DATE:

HOW HE _____

HOW SHE _____

HER DAY _____

HIS DAY _____

DATE:

HOW HE _____

HOW SHE _____

HER DAY _____

HIS DAY _____

"Don't ever stop dating your wife and don't ever
stop flirting with your husband." -Unknown

TODAY, I'M THANKFUL FOR...

DATE:

HOW HE

HOW SHE

HER DAY

HIS DAY

DATE:

HOW HE

HOW SHE

HER DAY

HIS DAY

DATE:

HOW HE

HOW SHE

HER DAY

HIS DAY

DATE:

HOW HE _____

HOW SHE _____

HER DAY _____

HIS DAY _____

DATE:

HOW HE _____

HOW SHE _____

HER DAY _____

HIS DAY _____

DATE:

HOW HE _____

HOW SHE _____

HER DAY _____

HIS DAY _____

"A good marriage is a contest of generosity." -Diane Sawyer

TODAY, I'M THANKFUL FOR...

DATE:

HOW HE

HOW SHE

HER DAY

HIS DAY

DATE:

HOW HE

HOW SHE

HER DAY

HIS DAY

DATE:

HOW HE

HOW SHE

HER DAY

HIS DAY

DATE:

HOW HE _____

HOW SHE _____

HER DAY _____

HIS DAY _____

DATE:

HOW HE _____

HOW SHE _____

HER DAY _____

HIS DAY _____

DATE:

HOW HE _____

HOW SHE _____

HER DAY _____

HIS DAY _____

"A perfect marriage is just two imperfect people
who refuse to give up on each other." -Unknown

TODAY, I'M THANKFUL FOR...

DATE:

HOW HE _____

HOW SHE _____

HER DAY _____

HIS DAY _____

DATE:

HOW HE _____

HOW SHE _____

HER DAY _____

HIS DAY _____

DATE:

HOW HE _____

HOW SHE _____

HER DAY _____

HIS DAY _____

DATE:

HOW HE _____

HOW SHE _____

HER DAY _____

HIS DAY _____

DATE:

HOW HE _____

HOW SHE _____

HER DAY _____

HIS DAY _____

DATE:

HOW HE _____

HOW SHE _____

HER DAY _____

HIS DAY _____

"A good marriage is good for you. That isn't just a platitude. Mounting research shows that it is the literal truth. When your marriage is healthy, your body and mind are healthier." -Cliff Isaacson

TODAY, I'M THANKFUL FOR...

DATE:

HOW HE

HOW SHE

HER DAY

HIS DAY

DATE:

HOW HE

HOW SHE

HER DAY

HIS DAY

DATE:

HOW HE

HOW SHE

HER DAY

HIS DAY

DATE:

HOW HE _____

HOW SHE _____

HER DAY _____

HIS DAY _____

DATE:

HOW HE _____

HOW SHE _____

HER DAY _____

HIS DAY _____

DATE:

HOW HE _____

HOW SHE _____

HER DAY _____

HIS DAY _____

"Marriage is like watching the color of leaves in the fall; ever changing and more stunningly beautiful with each passing day." -Fawn Weaver

TODAY, I'M THANKFUL FOR...

DATE:

HOW HE

HOW SHE

HER DAY

HIS DAY

DATE:

HOW HE

HOW SHE

HER DAY

HIS DAY

DATE:

HOW HE

HOW SHE

HER DAY

HIS DAY

DATE:

HOW HE _____

HOW SHE _____

HER DAY _____

HIS DAY _____

DATE:

HOW HE _____

HOW SHE _____

HER DAY _____

HIS DAY _____

DATE:

HOW HE _____

HOW SHE _____

HER DAY _____

HIS DAY _____

"Marriage: If you want something to last forever, you treat it differently. You shield it and protect it. You never abuse it. You don't expose it to the elements. It becomes special because you have made it so, and it grows more beautiful and precious as time goes by." -F. Burton Howard

TODAY, I'M THANKFUL FOR...

DATE:

HOW HE

HOW SHE

HER DAY

HIS DAY

DATE:

HOW HE

HOW SHE

HER DAY

HIS DAY

DATE:

HOW HE

HOW SHE

HER DAY

HIS DAY

DATE:

HOW HE _____

HOW SHE _____

HER DAY _____

HIS DAY _____

DATE:

HOW HE _____

HOW SHE _____

HER DAY _____

HIS DAY _____

DATE:

HOW HE _____

HOW SHE _____

HER DAY _____

HIS DAY _____

"The difference between an ordinary marriage and an extraordinary marriage is in giving just a little extra every day, as often as possible, for as long as we both shall live." -Fawn Weaver

TODAY, I'M THANKFUL FOR...

DATE:

HOW HE

HOW SHE

HER DAY

HIS DAY

DATE:

HOW HE

HOW SHE

HER DAY

HIS DAY

DATE:

HOW HE

HOW SHE

HER DAY

HIS DAY

DATE:

HOW HE _____

HOW SHE _____

HER DAY _____

HIS DAY _____

DATE:

HOW HE _____

HOW SHE _____

HER DAY _____

HIS DAY _____

DATE:

HOW HE _____

HOW SHE _____

HER DAY _____

HIS DAY _____

"Marriage doesn't make you happy–you make your marriage happy." -Drs. Les & Leslie Parrott

TODAY, I'M THANKFUL FOR...

DATE:

HOW HE

HOW SHE

HER DAY

HIS DAY

DATE:

HOW HE

HOW SHE

HER DAY

HIS DAY

DATE:

HOW HE

HOW SHE

HER DAY

HIS DAY

DATE:

HOW HE _____

HOW SHE _____

HER DAY _____

HIS DAY _____

DATE:

HOW HE _____

HOW SHE _____

HER DAY _____

HIS DAY _____

DATE:

HOW HE _____

HOW SHE _____

HER DAY _____

HIS DAY _____

"The best time to love with your whole heart is always now, in this moment, because no breath beyond the current is promised." -Fawn Weaver

TODAY, I'M THANKFUL FOR...

DATE:

HOW HE

HOW SHE

HER DAY

HIS DAY

DATE:

HOW HE

HOW SHE

HER DAY

HIS DAY

DATE:

HOW HE

HOW SHE

HER DAY

HIS DAY

DATE:

HOW HE

HOW SHE

HER DAY

HIS DAY

DATE:

HOW HE

HOW SHE

HER DAY

HIS DAY

DATE:

HOW HE

HOW SHE

HER DAY

HIS DAY

"Love doesn't make the world go round. Love is what
makes the ride worthwhile." -Franklin P. Jones

TODAY, I'M THANKFUL FOR...

DATE:

HOW HE

HOW SHE

HER DAY

HIS DAY

DATE:

HOW HE

HOW SHE

HER DAY

HIS DAY

DATE:

HOW HE

HOW SHE

HER DAY

HIS DAY

DATE:

HOW HE _____

HOW SHE _____

HER DAY _____

HIS DAY _____

DATE:

HOW HE _____

HOW SHE _____

HER DAY _____

HIS DAY _____

DATE:

HOW HE _____

HOW SHE _____

HER DAY _____

HIS DAY _____

"The greatest marriages are built on teamwork. A mutual respect, a healthy dose of admiration, and a never-ending portion of love and grace." -Fawn Weaver

TODAY, I'M THANKFUL FOR...

DATE:

HOW HE

HOW SHE

HER DAY

HIS DAY

DATE:

HOW HE

HOW SHE

HER DAY

HIS DAY

DATE:

HOW HE

HOW SHE

HER DAY

HIS DAY

DATE:

HOW HE _____

HOW SHE _____

HER DAY _____

HIS DAY _____

DATE:

HOW HE _____

HOW SHE _____

HER DAY _____

HIS DAY _____

DATE:

HOW HE _____

HOW SHE _____

HER DAY _____

HIS DAY _____

"Once we figured out that we could not change each other, we became free to celebrate ourselves as we are." -H. Dean Rutherford

TODAY, I'M THANKFUL FOR...

DATE:

HOW HE

HOW SHE

HER DAY

HIS DAY

DATE:

HOW HE

HOW SHE

HER DAY

HIS DAY

DATE:

HOW HE

HOW SHE

HER DAY

HIS DAY

DATE:

HOW HE _____

HOW SHE _____

HER DAY _____

HIS DAY _____

DATE:

HOW HE _____

HOW SHE _____

HER DAY _____

HIS DAY _____

DATE:

HOW HE _____

HOW SHE _____

HER DAY _____

HIS DAY _____

"A long-lasting marriage is built by two people who believe in -and live by- the solemn promise they made." -Darlene Schacht

TODAY, I'M THANKFUL FOR...

DATE:

HOW HE

HOW SHE

HER DAY

HIS DAY

DATE:

HOW HE

HOW SHE

HER DAY

HIS DAY

DATE:

HOW HE

HOW SHE

HER DAY

HIS DAY

DATE:

HOW HE _____

HOW SHE _____

HER DAY _____

HIS DAY _____

DATE:

HOW HE _____

HOW SHE _____

HER DAY _____

HIS DAY _____

DATE:

HOW HE _____

HOW SHE _____

HER DAY _____

HIS DAY _____

"To keep your marriage brimming, with love in the wedding cup, whenever you're wrong, admit it; whenever you're right, shut up." -Ogden Nash

TODAY, I'M THANKFUL FOR...

DATE:

HOW HE

HOW SHE

HER DAY

HIS DAY

DATE:

HOW HE

HOW SHE

HER DAY

HIS DAY

DATE:

HOW HE

HOW SHE

HER DAY

HIS DAY

DATE:

HOW HE _____

HOW SHE _____

HER DAY _____

HIS DAY _____

DATE:

HOW HE _____

HOW SHE _____

HER DAY _____

HIS DAY _____

DATE:

HOW HE _____

HOW SHE _____

HER DAY _____

HIS DAY _____

"They say it takes a village to raise a child. That may be the case, but the truth is that it takes a lot of solid, stable marriages to create a village." -Diane Sollee

TODAY, I'M THANKFUL FOR...

DATE:

HOW HE

HOW SHE

HER DAY

HIS DAY

DATE:

HOW HE

HOW SHE

HER DAY

HIS DAY

DATE:

HOW HE

HOW SHE

HER DAY

HIS DAY

DATE:

HOW HE _____

HOW SHE _____

HER DAY _____

HIS DAY _____

DATE:

HOW HE _____

HOW SHE _____

HER DAY _____

HIS DAY _____

DATE:

HOW HE _____

HOW SHE _____

HER DAY _____

HIS DAY _____

"The greatest weakness of most humans is their hesitancy to tell others how much they love them while they're still alive." -Orlando Battista

TODAY, I'M THANKFUL FOR...

DATE:

HOW HE

HOW SHE

HER DAY

HIS DAY

DATE:

HOW HE

HOW SHE

HER DAY

HIS DAY

DATE:

HOW HE

HOW SHE

HER DAY

HIS DAY

DATE:

HOW HE _____

HOW SHE _____

HER DAY _____

HIS DAY _____

DATE:

HOW HE _____

HOW SHE _____

HER DAY _____

HIS DAY _____

DATE:

HOW HE _____

HOW SHE _____

HER DAY _____

HIS DAY _____

"Your priorities aren't what you SAY they are. They are revealed by how you live. What does your life say about the value of your family and marriage?" -Marriage Today

TODAY, I'M THANKFUL FOR...

DATE:

HOW HE _____

HOW SHE _____

HER DAY _____

HIS DAY _____

DATE:

HOW HE _____

HOW SHE _____

HER DAY _____

HIS DAY _____

DATE:

HOW HE _____

HOW SHE _____

HER DAY _____

HIS DAY _____

DATE:

HOW HE _____

HOW SHE _____

HER DAY _____

HIS DAY _____

DATE:

HOW HE _____

HOW SHE _____

HER DAY _____

HIS DAY _____

DATE:

HOW HE _____

HOW SHE _____

HER DAY _____

HIS DAY _____

"The greatest favour we can do our children is to give
visible example of love and esteem to our spouse. As
they grow up, they may then look forward to maturity
so they too can find such love." -Eucharista Ward

TODAY, I'M THANKFUL FOR...

DATE:

HOW HE

HOW SHE

HER DAY

HIS DAY

DATE:

HOW HE

HOW SHE

HER DAY

HIS DAY

DATE:

HOW HE

HOW SHE

HER DAY

HIS DAY

DATE:

HOW HE _____

HOW SHE _____

HER DAY _____

HIS DAY _____

DATE:

HOW HE _____

HOW SHE _____

HER DAY _____

HIS DAY _____

DATE:

HOW HE _____

HOW SHE _____

HER DAY _____

HIS DAY _____

"Lean on each other's strengths. Forgive
each other's weaknesses." -Unknown

TODAY, I'M THANKFUL FOR...

DATE:

HOW HE

HOW SHE

HER DAY

HIS DAY

DATE:

HOW HE

HOW SHE

HER DAY

HIS DAY

DATE:

HOW HE

HOW SHE

HER DAY

HIS DAY

DATE:

HOW HE _____

HOW SHE _____

HER DAY _____

HIS DAY _____

DATE:

HOW HE _____

HOW SHE _____

HER DAY _____

HIS DAY _____

DATE:

HOW HE _____

HOW SHE _____

HER DAY _____

HIS DAY _____

"Marriages, like a garden, take time to grow. But the harvest is rich unto those who patiently and tenderly care for the ground." -Darlene Schacht

thank you!

We so appreciate reviews if you could leave us one

• • • •

DISCOVER MORE TITLES FROM
CREATIVE IDEAS PUBLISHING

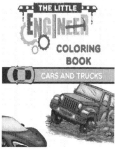

Made in the USA
Monee, IL
15 August 2022